THE GINN BASIC READERS

The Little White House

ODILLE OUSLEY · DAVID H. RUSSELL

GINN AND COMPANY

100 EDITION

Stories in This Book

Home

PAGE

At Home 6
Flip and Susan 9
Flip Wants to Help 13
The Little Chairs 17
A Surprise for Father 23
The Funny Bunny 27

The Pets

Something for Cathy 32
The Kitten at Home 35
Come Down, Tiger 39
Tiger and Jip 43
Cowboy Tom 47
The Truck Ride 53

Birthday Surprises

The Birthday Wagon 60
A Birthday Cake 65
Birthdays Are Fun 71
Ready to Go 77
At the Toy Store 82

At the Farm

On the Train 88
The Big Train 92
A Party in the Barn 97
Tom and Mr. T. Turkey 101
In the Barn *by Maud Lindsay* 108
Ready to Go Home 115

The New Toys

The Toy Duck 120
The Toy Mouse *by Nicholas Radlov* 123
The Toy Boat 127
The Race 131

Fun for You and Me

The Kittens' Dinner 136
Mr. Gobble-Gobble 141
Little Red Hen 147
The Mouse in the Play House 154

Fun at Home and Away

To Cathy's House 160
Fun with Cathy and Bob 165
Who Is Big? *by Martha Cranford* 167
Funny Surprises 173
Susan Helps, Too 177
Poem—Our House *by Dorothy Brown Thompson* 182
Review Pages 184

4

Home

At Home

Tom said, " Mother ! Mother !
Is Susan here ?
Is Susan at home ? "

Betty said, "Tom! Tom!
Look at Flip!
Look, Tom, look!
See Flip go."

"Look, Tom!" said Betty.
"Flip sees Susan.
Susan is here."

"I see Susan," said Tom.
"Susan is at home."

Flip and Susan

"Look, Betty!" said Tom.
"I see something.
I see something big."

Betty said, "Look at Flip.
Flip sees something.
Flip sees something big."

9

" Betty ! Tom ! " said Susan.
" See Flip ! See Flip ! "

" Flip ! Flip ! " said Tom.
" Come here, Flip.
Come here now."

Tom said, "Betty! Betty!
Look at Flip now!
See Flip go!"

Betty said, "Flip! Flip!
You are funny.
You are big and funny.
Go, Flip, go!"

11

" Mother ! Mother ! " said Betty.

" Come and see Susan.

Look at Susan ! "

" Look, Mother," said Susan.

" Look at this !

This is not funny.

Flip is not funny."

12

Flip Wants to Help

Betty said, " Come here, Tom.
Come and see Father.
See Father paint."

" Father ! Father ! " said Tom.
" I want to help.
I want to help you paint."

Father said, " Here, Tom.
You are ready now.
You can paint here."

" I can paint," said Betty.
" I want to paint something."

Tom said, " Betty ! Betty !
You can not paint now.
You are not ready."

14

Father said, " Get ready, Betty.
Go and get ready to paint.
You can help here.
You can paint something."

" Here I go ! " said Betty.
" I can get ready.
I can get ready fast."

15

Tom said, "Betty! Betty!
Look at Flip.
See the red paint.
Flip wants to help.
See Flip paint this red."

"Flip! Flip!" said Betty.
"You can not help here.
You can not paint."

16

The Little Chairs

" Come here, Tom," said Mother.
" Come fast, Betty and Susan.
Here is something for you.
Come and see the chairs."

" Little chairs ! " said Tom.
" I like the little chairs ! "

Betty said, " This is my chair.
This chair is for you, Susan."

Mother said, " Look at this.
Here is something you like.
Look at this red paint.
See the blue paint and green paint.
Now you can paint the little chairs.
You can surprise Father."

18

"Red! Red!" said Tom.
"I like this color.
I like a red chair."

"I like this color," said Susan.
"See my little green chair."

Betty said, "I like blue paint.
Blue is the color I like."

19

Tom said, " Father ! Father !
Come and see what is here."

Betty said, " We can paint.
We can paint chairs.
Come and see the little chairs."

Father said, " Little chairs !
Can you paint chairs ?
What a surprise ! "

20

" Guess, Father," said Betty.
" What color is my chair ? "

" Guess, guess ! " said Susan.
" We want you to guess."

" Can you guess, Father ? " said Tom.
" What color is my chair ? "

21

Father said, " I can guess, Tom.
I see red paint here.
You have a red chair.

" Look at this, Susan.
See the green paint.
You have a green chair.

" I see something blue here.
You have a blue chair, Betty.
Now I want to see the chairs."

A Surprise for Father

" Come, Father," said Bob.

" Come to the big green chair.

We have a surprise for you."

" Get down, Jip," said Father.

" You are in my big green chair.

I want my chair now.

I want to see my surprise."

Bob said, " Come, Cathy and Nancy.
Father is ready now.
Can you get the big box down ?
Is the surprise ready for Father ? "

Cathy said, " Here is the box, Bob.
The big box is ready for Father.
The surprise is in this box."

24

"What is this?" said Father.
"I see a big white box.
Is this my surprise?"

Bob said, "Look in the box.
See what is in the white box.
Look at the surprise, Father."

25

" Look, Mother ! " said Father.

" Look in this white box.

Here is something blue.

Blue is the color I like.

What a good surprise !

What a good chair !

What a good home ! "

26

The Funny Bunny

"Look here, Father," said Cathy.
"I have something in here.
Can you guess what I have?"

"I can guess," said Father.
"I can guess what you have.
You have Teddy."

27

"What a good guess!" said Cathy.
"Here is Teddy."

"Now look, Father," said Bob.
"Guess what I have down here.
This is something we like."

"I can guess," said Father.
"You have Jip."

"What is this?" said Mother.
"Can you guess what I have?"

"I can guess," said Bob.
"You have a bunny."

"Not a bunny!" said Mother.
"A bunny is not here."

"Now look, Bob!" said Mother.
"You can see what is here now."

"Nancy!" said Bob.
"Now I can see Nancy!
What a good surprise!"

"Funny Nancy!" said Father.
"You are a funny bunny."

30

The Pets

Something for Cathy

Father said, " Look here, Cathy.
I have something for you.
Guess what I have.
Guess what is in this box."

Cathy said, " A hat!
This looks like a box for a hat.
A hat is in this box! "

" Mew ! " said something in the box.

" Mew, mew, mew ! "

" Now I can guess," said Cathy.

" This is not a hat.

Is this a box for a pet ?

Something in the box said, ' Mew ! '

Is a pet in this box, Father ? "

Father said, "Look in the box.
Look in the box and see."

"A little kitten!" said Cathy.
"What a good pet!
I like my little pet."

"Mew, mew!" said the kitten.
"Mew, mew, mew!"

34

The Kitten at Home

"Bob! Nancy!" said Cathy.
"Will you come here?
Come and see what I have.
See what is in my box!"

Bob said, "Here we come.
We will come fast.
We want to see what you have."

"Look, Bob, look!" said Nancy.
"Look at the kitten.
What a little kitten!
I like this pet."

"Look, Nancy!" said Bob.
"See the kitten run to Cathy.
The kitten likes Cathy."

36

"Bob! Bob!" said Cathy.

"See my little kitten run.

See my kitten run to the tree.

Will you get my kitten, Bob?"

Bob said, "Here I go.

I will get the kitten."

37

Bob said, "Look up in the tree.
See the kitten go up the tree."

"My, my!" said Father.
"What a fast little kitten!
This tiger kitten can run fast."

"Tiger Kitten!" said Cathy.
"You are Tiger Kitten.
You are my little pet."

Come Down, Tiger

Cathy said, "Come down, Tiger.
Will you please come down?"

"Tiger! Tiger!" said Nancy.
"Please come down now.
Come down and see Teddy."

"Mew, mew," said Tiger Kitten.

39

"Father! Father!" said Bob.
"Tiger is up in the tree.
Tiger will not come down."

Cathy said, "Please, Father!
Please do something to help.
Little Tiger is in the big tree.
We want Tiger to come down.
Please go up and get Tiger."

40

Father went to the tree.

"I will help," said Father.
"See what I can do.
I can go up the tree.
I will get Tiger."

Father went up the tree.
Up and up he went.

"Now look at Tiger!" said Cathy.
"See Tiger come down.
Look at Father up in the tree.
And look at Tiger down here.
Tiger, you are a funny kitten."

42

Tiger and Jip

" Come here, Jip," said Bob.

" Come and play here.

Come and see the kitten.

Come and see Tiger."

Jip said, " Bow-wow ! Bow-wow ! "

Tiger said, " Mew, mew ! "

43

Cathy said, "Tiger! Tiger!
Please do not run away.
Jip likes you, Tiger.
He wants to play."

Away went Tiger.
Away went Jip.

"Stop, Jip, stop!" said Bob.
"Come here, Jip!"

Tiger went fast.

Jip went fast.

"Bow-wow! Bow-wow!" he said.

Bob said, "Look at Tiger now.

What can we do?"

"Come down, Tiger," said Cathy.

"You are not a good kitten."

Bob said, " Look, Cathy !
See Jip now.
See what Tiger did to Jip ! "

" Tiger !   Tiger ! " said Cathy.
" Look at Jip.
See what you did to Jip ! "

46

Cowboy Tom

"Go fast, Flip," said Tom.
"Run fast, Pony.
We will play cowboy."

Flip and Pony did go fast.
And Cowboy Tom went fast.
Away he went for a fast ride.

Up went the cowboy hat.
It went up and up.

"My hat! My hat!" said Tom.
"Stop, Pony! Stop!
We can not play cowboy now.
I do not have my hat."

48

"Tom!" said Mr. Green.
"I see the big cowboy hat.
It is up in this tree."

Tom said, "I see my hat now.
Pony and I went for a fast ride.
My cowboy hat went up and up.
I want to get my cowboy hat.
What can I do, Mr. Green?"

" Come, Tom," said Mr. Green.
" Come here, Cowboy Tom.
My truck and I can help you.
We will help you get the hat."

" Here I come ! " said Tom.
" Now what can I do to help ? "

" Get up here," said Mr. Green.
" You can get up in my truck."

Up in the truck went Cowboy Tom.

Up in the truck he went.

"Now I can get it," said Tom.

"I can get my cowboy hat."

"Good for you," said Mr. Green.

"Good for you, Cowboy Tom.

You did get the big hat."

" Mr. Green ! " said Tom.
"You are good to help.
I did not want my hat in a tree.
Now I can play cowboy."

" Good ! " said Mr. Green.
" My truck and I like to help.
We like to help cowboys."

52

The Truck Ride

Away went the big blue truck.

Away went Mr. Green.

Mr. Green and the truck went fast.

Mr. Green said, " I will stop here.

Here are the airplanes.

I have a box for a big airplane."

Mr. Green went to the truck.
He went to get the box.

Something said, " Bow-wow!
Bow-wow, bow-wow ! "

" What is it ? " said Mr. Green.
" What is in my truck ?
It is a dog !
It is Flip in my truck ! "

" Bow-wow ! Bow-wow ! " said Flip.
Then away he went.

Mr. Green said, " Stop, Flip !
Do not run away.
Dogs can not run and play here.
Airplanes come and go here.
See the big airplane.
It is ready to go."

Zoom! went the big airplane.
Zoom! Zoom! Zoom!
Then away the airplane went.
Zoom!

"Bow-wow, bow-wow!" said Flip.
Away he went to Mr. Green.
Away Flip went to the truck.
He went fast!

" You funny dog ! " said Mr. Green.

" You do not like airplanes.

Get in the truck, Flip.

Do you want to go home now ?

Do you want to see the children ? "

" Bow-wow, bow-wow ! " said Flip.

Flip did want to go home.

He did want to see the children.

Away went Flip and Mr. Green.

Mr. Green said, " Here we are, Flip.
Do you see the children ? "

" Bow-wow ! " said Flip.
He went to the children fast !

Mr. Green said, " Flip went
for a ride in my truck.
He went to see the airplanes.
He did not like the big airplanes.
Flip likes it here
at the little white house."

Birthday Surprises

The Birthday Wagon

"Look, Betty!" said Susan.
"Look at the red birthday wagon.
Red is the color Tom likes.
He will like this big red wagon."

"The wagon is ready," said Father.
"Are you ready, Susan?
You can surprise Tom now!"

60

" Go now, Susan," said Father.

" You and the wagon can go to Tom.

We do not want Tom to see you.

We want Tom to see the wagon.

We want to surprise Tom."

" Go fast, Susan ! " said Betty.

" Go and surprise Tom !

Birthday surprises are fun."

61

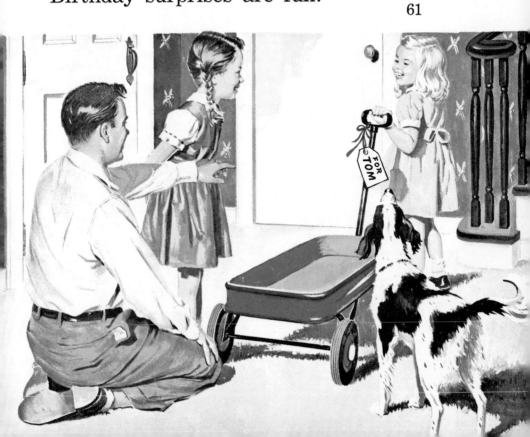

" Here I go," said Susan.

" This is fun.

I like to surprise Tom."

Susan saw Tom.

Tom did not see Susan.

He did not see the wagon.

He did not see Flip.

" Surprise, Tom ! " said Susan.

" See the big red wagon !
It is a birthday surprise ! "

Tom saw the birthday wagon.

" What a good surprise ! " he said.

" I like my birthday wagon !
I can make this wagon go fast."

63

"Look at Flip!" said Susan.
"Flip likes the big red wagon.
He wants to go for a ride in it."

"Funny Flip!" said Tom.
"This wagon is not for you.
It is my birthday wagon.
You and I will have fun
in this wagon.
We will make it go fast."

64

A Birthday Cake

Mother said, " See this white cake.
Tom likes white cake.
This is a birthday cake for Tom.
We will surprise Tom."

Susan saw the birthday cake.
" I want to help," she said.
" I want to help surprise Tom.
We will have fun."

Mother said, " See the candles.
Look at the birthday cake now.
Tom likes red birthday candles."

Susan saw the candles.
" What little candles ! " she said.
" I like white cake and red candles.
I want to help you, Mother.
I can help you do this."
66

"Come, Mother!" said Betty.
"Please come here.
I want you to see something.
It is something for Tom's birthday."

Mother said, "I can come now.
The birthday cake is ready."

67

Susan did not go.
She saw the birthday cake.
She saw the red candles.

" I will help Mother," said Susan.
" I will put this little candle here.
I will put candles here and here.
Tom likes red candles."

68

Susan said, "Mother! Mother!
See what I did!
See the red candles now.
Come and see the birthday cake.
It is ready for the party."

Betty said, "Look, Mother, look!
See the candles!"

69

Mother saw the birthday cake.
She saw candles and candles.

"Susan! Susan!" she said.
"Tom is seven.
He will want seven candles.
We will put seven candles here.
Now we are ready for the party."

70

Birthdays Are Fun

" Come in," said Betty.

" Come in the house.

Come to the party.

We will surprise Tom.

He is seven now."

" Good! Good!" said Nan.

" A surprise party is fun."

" Surprise, Tom ! " said Jack.

" Surprise ! Surprise ! " said Cathy.

" We have come to the party.

A birthday party for you ! "

" A birthday party ? " said Tom.

" What a good surprise !

A birthday party is fun ! "

72

" What is this ? " said Tom.

" What is in this box ? "

Mother said, " Birthday hats !
The hats are for your party."

Tom said, " Look at the hats !
I want Bob and Jack
to have red hats."

Tom said, "Look now!
Cathy and Nan want blue hats.
This white hat is for Betty, and
the green hat is for Susan."

Susan said, "I like the green hat.
This is the hat I want."

"Where is my hat?" said Tom.
"I do not have a birthday hat.
Where is my hat?"

"Look here," said Tom.
"I can make a hat.
I like my birthday hat.
It is funny."

"Look, Cathy," said Bob.
"Tom has a hat.
Tom can make a hat."

Cathy said, "Tom has a good hat.
I like your birthday hat, Tom."

"Come, children," said Mother.
"The party is ready."

"This party is fun," said Tom.
"See my birthday cake!
It has seven red candles."

Then the children said,
   "Happy birthday to you.
   Happy birthday to you.
   Happy birthday to Tom.
   Happy birthday to you!"

76

Ready to Go

Tom said, "Look at this!
My uncle has put a surprise
in here.
Is it something for my birthday?"

Mother said, "It is for a toy.
You can get a birthday toy.
Do you want to go and get it now?
Get ready and we will go."

Betty said, " Come here, Susan!
See what Tom has!
See what Uncle Fred put in here.
Uncle Fred wants Tom to get a toy.
We want to get the toy now.
Do you want to come ? "

" I do ! " said Susan.
" I like to go to see the toys.
I will get ready fast."
78

Mother said, " Are we ready now ?

Tom is ready to go to the toy store.

You look ready to go, Betty.

Where is Susan ? "

" Susan ! Susan ! " said Betty.

" Where are you ?

Please come down now.

We are ready to go to the toy store."

79

" Here I come," said Susan.
" I went to get my hat.
I like this green birthday hat."

Tom and Betty saw Susan.
They saw the funny hat.

" Look at Susan ! " said Tom.
" See the birthday hat.
Susan is not ready to go."

Betty and Mother saw the hat.
They laughed and laughed.
And Susan laughed.

" Come here, Susan," said Mother.
"The green hat is a party hat.
We will put it away now.
This red hat is what you want.
Now you are ready to go
to the toy store."

81

At the Toy Store

" Here we are," said Tom.

" Here we are at the toy store.

I know what I want to get.

Do you know what it is ?

Can you guess ? "

"I know! I know!" said Betty.
"It is this big airplane.
Is this what you want?"

"I have a toy airplane," Tom said.
"I can see the toy I want now.
I can make this toy go fast.
Do you know what it is?"

Susan said, "I will guess.

Is it the little blue truck?

Is it the green and white ball?

What color is it?"

"Look at the toys here," said Tom.

"You can see the toy I want.

It is black and red.

It can go fast.

Now can you guess?"

84

Mother laughed.

" I can guess," she said.

" It is not the ball.

Tom has a ball.

It is not the truck.

This toy is red and black.

Tom will have fun with it."

85

" The train ! " said Betty.

" You want the little train.

I like this black and red train."

Tom laughed and said,

" You did guess what I want.

I want the red and black train.

I like to play with trains.

A train is a good birthday toy.

Uncle Fred will like this train."

At the Farm

87

On the Train

"Here we go," said Father.
"Here we go to the farm.
Away we go on the big train."

Tom said, "This is fun.
I like to ride on the train.
I like to go to the farm."

Susan said, " Go fast, big train.

Please go fast.

I want to see my aunt.

I want to see Uncle Fred."

Betty said, " Look at Patsy.

Patsy and Bunny are happy.

They like to ride on the train.

They want to go to the farm."

Father said, " What is in the box ?
Is it something for Uncle Fred ?
Is it something for Aunt Mary ? "

Tom said, " It is my toy train.
I want Uncle Fred to see it.
And I want Aunt Mary to see it.
I know they like toy trains.
We can play train at the farm."
90

Away went the little toy train.

"Tom! Tom!" said Father.

"See your train go.

Go and get your train."

"Here is your train!" said Mr. Bell.

"I like this little train.

Can it go fast?"

"My train can go fast," said Tom.

"And your big train can go fast."

The Big Train

Mr. Bell said, " Come, Tom.
Do you want to see my big train ?
Can you come now ? "

Betty and Susan saw Mr. Bell.
" Please ! Please ! " said Betty.
" Susan and I want to go with you.
We want to see your big train, too."

The children went with Mr. Bell.
The children went to see the train.

"What a big train!" said Tom.
"I like to ride on this train."

"I have a surprise for you,"
said Mr. Bell.
"Look in here.
Do you see your surprise?"

" Flip ! Flip ! " said Betty.

" You are the surprise !

We are happy to see you."

Flip jumped up.

He jumped on the children.

" Bow-wow, bow-wow ! " he said.

" Look at Flip," said Tom.

" He is a happy dog now.

He likes to ride on trains, too."

" Thank you, Mr. Bell," said Betty.
" Thank you for the good surprise.
We do like your big train."

" We are here now," said Father.
" We have to get ready to go."

" Mother ! Father ! " said Susan.
" I can see Uncle Fred.
I can see Aunt Mary."

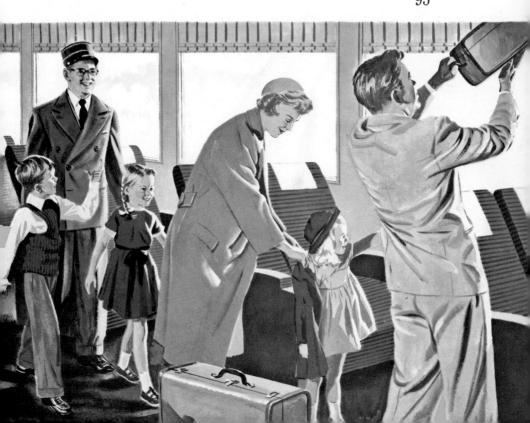

"Thank you, Mr. Bell," said Tom.
"Thank you for the train ride."

"Come, children," said Mother.
"Father has to go and get Flip.
Do you see Aunt Mary?"

Susan jumped up and down.
She said, "Aunt Mary! Uncle Fred!
Here we are!"

A Party in the Barn

" Here we are," said Uncle Fred.

" Here we are at the farm."

" Come on, Susan," said Tom.

" Come to the barn.

I want you to see something.

It is something you like."

" I know what it is," said Betty.

" I want to go to the barn, too."

" Pony ! " said Susan.

" Here is my Pony!
Pony is here in the barn ! "

" Good little Pony ! " said Betty.
" We have come to see you.
Do you like this big barn ?
Do you like it here at the farm ?
Are you happy here, Pony ?
Are you happy to see me ? "

"Pony is happy," said Uncle Fred.
"He likes this barn.
He likes it here with Big Red."

"Come to me, Pony," said Tom.
"I have something for you to eat.
Here is a big apple.
Eat this red apple, Pony."

"Look, Uncle Fred," said Betty.
"I have a good apple
for Big Red too."

Susan said, "Pony likes apples.
Big Red likes apples, too.
This is a party in the barn.
Pony and Big Red like the party."

Tom and Mr. T. Turkey

Uncle Fred said, " Here, Tom !
Come and help me work.
Put this in your big hat.
This is a dinner for Mr. T. Turkey.
Mr. T. Turkey wants dinner now."

Tom said, " I like to help.
I like to work on the farm."

Tom said, " Here I go !
I will take the dinner
to Mr. T. Turkey."
Away went Tom with the dinner.

Mr. T. Turkey saw Tom.
He saw something to eat.
Mr. T. Turkey went to Tom.
He went fast, fast !

102

"Mr. T. Turkey," said Tom.
"You run too fast.
This is your dinner.
I will not take it away."

"Gobble!" said Mr. T. Turkey.
"Gobble-gobble!"

" Stop ! Stop ! " said Tom.
" Stop, Mr. T. Turkey !
You come too fast."

But Mr. Turkey did not stop.
Down went Tom.
Down went the big hat.
Down went the dinner.

" Look, Tom ! " said Betty.

" See your cowboy hat now.

It is on Mr. T. Turkey !

And see Mr. T. Turkey run ! "

Tom jumped up.

He saw the hat on Mr. T. Turkey.

He saw Mr. T. Turkey run.

Tom ran, too.

Tom called to Mr. T. Turkey,
" Stop, Mr. T. Turkey, stop !
Stop and eat your dinner.
Do not run away with my hat ! "

" Gobble ! " said Mr. T. Turkey.
But Mr. T. Turkey did not stop.
On and on he ran.
Away went the hat
with Mr. T. Turkey.

106

" Look, Betty ! " called Tom.

" I will get my hat now.

It is my good cowboy hat.

I like it."

Betty laughed.

" You like it," she said.

" But Mr. T. Turkey did not like it.

See Mr. T. Turkey run ! "

In the Barn

" Run to the barn, children,"
said Uncle Fred.

" The kittens are in the barn."

" The kittens will play
with you," said Aunt Mary.

" Then come to the house
and we will eat dinner."

Tom called, " Come with me.
Come up, Susan and Betty.
Come up and see the kittens."

Susan and Betty went
up with Tom.
Up and up they went.

Susan looked for the kittens.
" Where are they ? " she said.
" I can not see the kittens."

Then something said, " Mew, mew."
" Mew, mew, mew," it said.

" Look in this box," said Tom.
" Can you see the kittens now ? "

The children looked at the kittens.

"I like this kitten," said Betty.

"She looks like a good kitten."

Susan said, "I like this kitten.

I will take this black kitten.

Come here, little kitten."

" Betty ! Susan ! " called Tom.
" Come here ! Come here !
Look at this !
See what Pony did !
Now we can not get down."

112

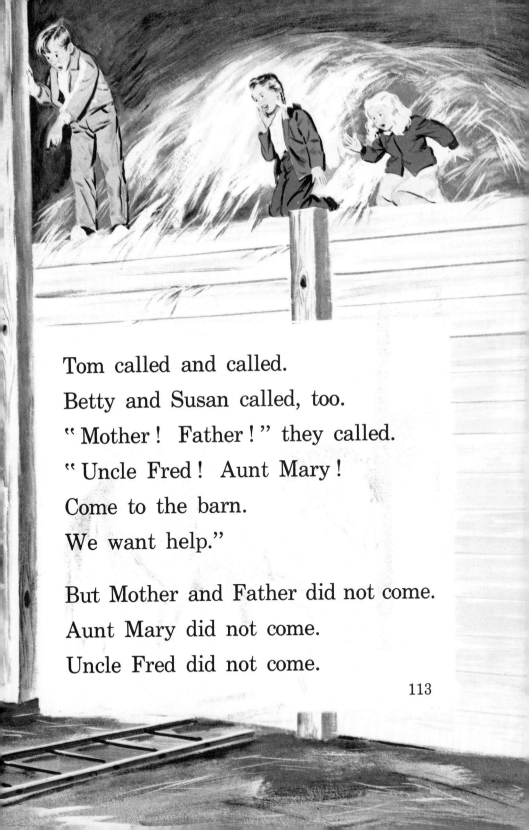

Tom called and called.

Betty and Susan called, too.

"Mother! Father!" they called.

"Uncle Fred! Aunt Mary!

Come to the barn.

We want help."

But Mother and Father did not come.

Aunt Mary did not come.

Uncle Fred did not come.

Then Tom saw Father.

"Father! Father!" called Tom.

"See what Pony did!

Will you please help, Father?"

"This will help," said Father.

"Now you can get down."

"Thank you," said the children.

114 "Now we can go to dinner!"

Ready to Go Home

" Now we can go," said Uncle Fred.
" We are ready to go to the train."

" Bow-wow ! " said Flip.
Then away he ran.

" Flip ! Flip ! " called Tom.
" Come here ! Come here to me.
We have to go to the train now.
Do not play with the ducks."

Mother said, " Where did Flip go ?
Did Flip go to get water ?
Did he go to play with the ducks ?
Please get Flip, Tom.
We are ready to go home."

Away ran Tom.
" Come here, Flip," he called.
" We are ready to go now."

" Here you are, Flip," said Tom.

" What do you want here?

You can not play now.

We have to go to the train.

I came to get you.

Come here, Flip!"

" Bow-wow!" said Flip.

Then he came fast to Tom.

Tom laughed and said,
"See what Flip has, Mother.
Flip did not go for water.
He did not go to play with the ducks.
He went to get something to eat.
And he wants to take it home."

"Now we are ready," said Betty.
"Thank you, Aunt Mary.
Thank you, Uncle Fred.
Thank you for the fun
at the farm."

118

The Toy Duck

Cathy said, " See my new toy duck.
I can make the toy duck walk.
It is ready to go now."

Away went the toy duck.
Walk! Walk! Walk!

"What a funny duck!" said Nancy.
"I like to see this duck walk.
Please make it walk to me."

120

"Go, Toy Duck," said Cathy.

"Walk to Nancy.

Go fast, Toy Duck.

We want to see you walk fast."

"Quack, quack," said Toy Duck.

"Quack, quack, quack."

Then away it went.

"This duck can quack," said Bob.

"It can walk and it can quack.

See the toy duck go!"

Bob said, " Look, Cathy !
See where your toy duck is now.
It is in the water.
It did not walk to Nancy.
The toy duck came to the water ! "

The children laughed.
" My toy duck is funny," said Cathy.
" It is like a farm duck.
It can walk and it can quack.
It likes water, too."
122

The Toy Mouse

" Here is a toy mouse, Nancy,"
said Mother.

" Tiger will like this mouse.

It is a toy mouse.

But it can run fast."

" Thank you, Mother," said Nancy.

" I will make this mouse run.

I will surprise Tiger with it."

The toy mouse ran and ran.
Tiger Kitten saw it run.
Away ran Tiger to get it.

" Cathy ! Bob ! " called Nancy.
" See my new toy mouse go !
See Tiger run to get it.
They look funny."

The children laughed and laughed.
Then Jip looked at the toy mouse.
Away he ran to get it.

124

" Bow-wow ! " said Jip.

" Bow-wow, bow-wow ! "

Then he jumped on the toy mouse.

" Stop, Jip, stop ! " called Cathy.

" The toy mouse is not for you.

You are too big to play

with this little mouse.

This new toy is for Tiger."

" Look here, Jip ! " called Bob.
" See what you did !
This toy mouse is for Tiger.
Now look at it !
It can not run now ! "

Father came and looked at the toy.
Then he said, " I can help.
I can make the mouse run.
But Jip is not to play with it.
This is not a good toy for Jip."

The Toy Boat

"Cathy! Nancy!" called Bob.
"Come and see my new toy boat.
It is a fast little boat.
Come in here and see
what it can do."

Bob put the new little boat
in the water.

Away went the little toy boat.
" Put-put-put," it said.

" See my boat go," said Bob.
" This is a good little boat.
It can go fast in the water."

Cathy said, " Look at the boat now.

Look at it come to me.

I will put my toy duck on it."

Cathy put the toy duck

on the boat.

" Put-put ! " said the toy boat.

Away went the little boat.

Away went the toy duck.

Nancy said, " My mouse can ride.
I will put my mouse on the boat."

Nancy put the mouse on the boat.
" Put-put-put ! " said the little boat.
Then down went the little toy boat.
Down went toy duck and toy mouse.
Down they went in the water.
130

The Race

" Betty ! Tom ! " said Cathy.
" Please come in.
Come in the house."

" We came to play," said Betty.
" We have new toys."

" New toys ! " said Bob.
" I can see Betty's blue airplane.
But your toy is in a box, Tom.
What do you have ? "

"My new train!" said Tom.

"I have my new red and black train in this box."

Bob said, "Can it go fast? My big black train can go fast."

"This big green truck will go fast," said Cathy.

"My blue airplane will go fast, too," said Betty.

132

" We can have a race," said Tom.

" The toys can race."

" A race ! A race ! " said the children.

" A toy race is fun," said Bob.

" We will get the toys ready."

Away went Bob's black train.

Away went Tom's little train.

Then away went the green truck.

Away went the blue airplane.

The blue airplane went
too fast for the big black train.
It went too fast
for Tom's little red and black train.
It went too fast
for the big green truck.
Zoom! Zoom! went the airplane.

"The airplane!" said the children.
"Did you see the airplane zoom?
What a good race!"

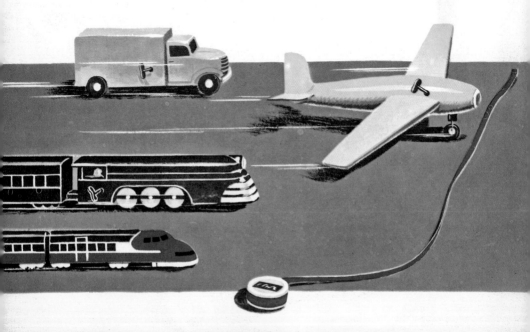

Fun for You and Me

The Kittens' Dinner

The little kittens went
to look for something to eat.
They looked and looked.

Yellow Kitten said,
" Mew, mew, mew !
I do not see a dinner here.
Do you ? "

136

Away went the little kittens.

Then they saw a good big dinner.

Yellow Kitten said, " Come and see.

I see some dinner

here at this tree."

Then Black Kitten said,
   " Your dinner is here.
   It is ready for you.
   But you can not eat it.
   Big Dog is here, too."

137

The little kittens looked at Big Dog.
Then they said,

"Mew, mew, mew, mew!

What can we do?

Big Dog will not go away.

He wants some of this dinner, too."

Then Black Kitten said,

"See what I have.

We can have some fun.

We can get the dinner.

We will make the big dog run."

The little kittens laughed and said,

"We know what you want to do.

We are ready to help you, too."

" MEW ! MEW ! " called the kittens.

Big Dog jumped up !
He did not stop to see who called.
He ran away fast ! Fast !

The kittens ran to get the dinner.
Then they said,
    " We did make the big dog run.
    My, my ! We did have fun ! "

Mr. Gobble-Gobble

"Bow-wow!" said Black Dog.
"Who are you?
And what do you do?"

"Gobble," said Mr. Gobble-Gobble.
"Gobble, gobble!"

"Bow-wow," said Black Dog.
"You are big, Mr. Gobble-Gobble.
But you are in a big box.
You can not get out of it.
You can not gobble me up."

Then up came White Kitten.

She looked in the box.

She saw the big turkey.

" Mew, mew ! " said White Kitten.

" Who are you ?

And what do you do ? "

The big turkey looked
at White Kitten.

"Gobble, gobble," he said.

"Gobble, gobble, gobble!"

"Mew, mew," said White Kitten.

"You are Mr. Gobble-Gobble.

But you can not gobble me up.

You can not get out of your box.

I can run and you can not."

143

Then up walked Yellow Duck.

" Quack, quack," she said.

" Who are you?

What do you do?"

" Gobble," said Mr. Gobble-Gobble.

" Gobble, gobble, gobble!"

" Quack, quack," said Yellow Duck.

" You can not gobble me up.

You can not get out of your box.

What a funny turkey you are!"

Then out of the box
walked Mr. Gobble-Gobble.
He came out fast.

" Look, look ! " called Black Dog.
" Mr. Gobble-Gobble is out
of the box.
What will he do now ? "

" Gobble ! " said Mr. Gobble-Gobble.
" I will gobble you up ! "

145

"Run, run!" said Black Dog.
"Run fast, White Kitten.
Run fast, Yellow Duck.
Run to the barn.
Run, run, run!"

And they did!

146

Little Red Hen

Little Red Hen walked to the farm.

She went to look for something

to eat.

"I will go to the barn," she said.

"I will look in the barn

for something good to eat."

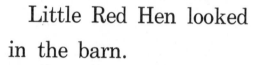

Little Red Hen looked
in the barn.

She saw a big duck.

She saw a big turkey.

Then she saw something yellow.

She ran to look at it.

"Wheat!" said Little Red Hen.

"This wheat will make something
good to eat."

148

"I will plant this wheat,"
said Little Red Hen.

"Who will help me
plant this wheat?"

"Not I," said the duck.

"Not I," said the turkey.

"I do not like to plant wheat."

"I will then," said Little Red Hen.

"I will plant this wheat."
And she did.

The wheat came up.

Little Red Hen said, " This wheat is ready to go to the mill.

Who will help me take this wheat to the mill ? "

" Not I," said the duck.

" Not I," said the turkey.

" I do not like to go to the mill."

" I will then," said Little Red Hen.

" I will take the wheat to the mill."

And she did.

"Now I will make some bread,"
said Little Red Hen.

"Who will help me make bread?"

"Not I," said the duck.

"Not I," said the turkey.

"I do not like to make bread."

"I will then," said Little Red Hen.

"I will make some bread."

151

"Look!" said Little Red Hen.
"The bread is ready now.
See what good bread it is.
Who will help to eat my bread?"

"I will," said the duck.
"I will," said the turkey.

But Little Red Hen said,

" You will not eat this bread.

You did not help me do the work.

You did not plant the wheat.

You did not take it to the mill.

You did not make the bread.

" My children and I
will eat this bread."

And they did !

The Mouse in the Play House

" Mother ! Mother ! "
called Little Mouse.
" Please come here, Mother.
What is this ?
Do you know what this is ? "

" Yes, yes," said Mother Mouse.
" This is a play house.
You can have fun in here."

154

"Mother! Mother!"
called Little Mouse.
"What is this?
May I play in this?"

"Yes, yes," said Mother Mouse.
"This is a toy airplane.
You may ride in the toy airplane."

Little Mouse jumped
in the toy airplane.
But the airplane did not go.
Little Mouse did not get a ride.

155

"Mother! Mother!"
said Little Mouse.
"What is this?
May I ride in this?"

"Yes, yes!" said Mother Mouse.
"This is a new wagon.
Get in the new yellow wagon."

Little Mouse jumped in the wagon.
But the yellow wagon did not go.
Little Mouse did not get a ride.

"Mother! Mother!"
called Little Mouse.
"Look here, Mother.
What is this?
May I ride in this?"

"My, my!" said Mother Mouse.
"I do not know.
I do not know what this is!
But get in it and see!"

157

Up jumped Little Mouse.
Then away he went fast.

"Stop! Stop!" called Mother Mouse.
"Please stop, Little Mouse!
I do not like this play house."

"But I do!" said Little Mouse.
"I like this play house, Mother.
I like this ride.
See me go!"

158

Fun at Home and Away

To Cathy's House

" See what I have, Betty," said Tom.

" See my big airplane !

I want Cathy and Bob to see it.

Do you want to go with me ?

Do you want to go to Cathy's house ? "

" Yes ! Yes ! " said Betty.

" I want to go."

"Do not go now, Tom," said Betty.
"I want to take Patsy with me.
I will go and get Patsy now."

"I will go in the house, too,"
said Tom.
"I want to get my ball and truck.
And I want something to eat."

161

Betty and Tom came out of the house.
"This is a good apple," said Tom.
"I like apples."

Tom put the ball in the wagon.
He put the truck in, too.
He said to Betty, "Now I can go.
Are you and Patsy ready to go?"

"Yes, we are ready," said Betty.
"Now we can go to Cathy's house."

162

Away walked Tom.

But he did not walk fast.

"Betty! Betty!" called Tom.

"This is my new wagon.

It will go fast.

But I can not make it go fast now.

What did you put in my wagon?"

"I put Patsy in it," said Betty.

"But Patsy is little.

She will not stop your wagon."

Tom and Betty looked
in the wagon.

"Look, Tom!" said Betty.
"Susan is in your big airplane."
Then they laughed and laughed.

"Please take me too," said Susan.
"I want to play at Nancy's."

"You may go, Susan," said Tom.
"But you will have to walk."

Fun with Cathy and Bob

The children went up to the house.
" Cathy ! Bob ! " they called.

" Come in ! Come in ! " said Cathy.
" Come in and see what we have.
We have something new in here."

" I can make it work," said Bob.
" Get ready for some fun now."

165

Bob said, " What do you like?
What do you like to see, Tom? "

" Cowboys! " said Tom.
" I like to look at cowboys."

" Pets! " said Susan.
" I like to look at funny pets."

" Here is something good," said Bob.
" You will like to look at this."

166

Who Is Big?

Yellow Kitten said to Black Hen,
" Mew, mew ! You are big ! "

Black Hen said, " A hen is not big.
Go and see Mr. Turkey.
He is big."

Yellow Kitten walked and walked.

Then she saw Mr. Turkey.

"Mew, mew," said Yellow Kitten.

"You are big, Mr. Turkey."

"Gobble! Gobble!" said Mr. Turkey.

"Turkeys are not big.

Go to the barn and see Black Pony.

He is big."

Yellow Kitten went to the barn.
She looked and looked.
Then she saw Black Pony.

Yellow Kitten said, "Mew, mew!
Black Pony is big! Big!
But look! Look!
Look at the little mouse!"

Then Mother Mouse saw the kitten.
"Run! Run!" called Mother Mouse.
"Run, Little Mouse!
Here is a big, big kitten.
Run, Little Mouse! Run!
The big kitten will get you!"

And Little Mouse did run.
Away he ran to Mother Mouse.

"Mew, mew!" said Yellow Kitten.

"The hen is big.

The turkey is big.

The pony is big.

And a kitten is big, too."

Then she walked like a big kitten.

She walked like a big, big kitten.

"Bow-wow-wow!" said Jip.
The children laughed.

"You funny dog!" said Cathy.
"You did not like the kittens.
You want to go out to play."

Tom said, "Thank you, Bob.
We like to look at this.
We like to come to your house."
172

Funny Surprises

Mother called,
" Come in here, children.
Nancy and I have surprises.
We have some surprises for you.
You will have to look
for the surprises."

" This is fun," said Tom.
" We will look up,
and we will look down.
We will look and look."

173

"Look, look!" called Cathy.
"I have a little hen.
It is little and red."

"Look up here!" said Tom.
"See my big green tree!
It looks like the tree at home."

"I have a little white boat,"
said Betty.

"Look at Bob!

He has a big yellow duck."

Susan said, "See my surprise!

It is a big bunny.

See me eat this bunny!"

" Look at Jip," said Bob.

" He has a surprise too.

He can eat and we can eat.

We can have a party."

" Thank you, Mother," said Cathy.

" Thank you, Nancy," said Bob.

" The surprises are good to eat.

We like this surprise party."

Susan Helps, Too

" Come, Betty and Susan," said Tom.
" We have to go home now."

Away walked the children.
Away they went with the wagon
and the toys.

Then Betty said, " Look !
Look, Tom ! Look, Susan !
I see something at the house ! "

177

"I see something, too," said Tom.

"Now I can see who has come
to the house.

Do you know who it is?"

"Yes, yes!" said Susan.

"It is Aunt Mary and Uncle Fred.
Run, Tom! Run fast, Betty!"

178

"Uncle Fred! Aunt Mary!"
called Betty.

"We are happy to see you."

Tom said, "Betty and I are big.
We can help you, Uncle Fred.
We can help you take something
to the house.
We have the wagon here."

"Thank you," said Uncle Fred.
"Aunt Mary and I do want help."

179

" See me work ! " said Susan.
" I can help, too."

" Aunt Mary ! " said Tom.
" See what Susan can do !
She has put something
on my toy truck.
She wants to take it to the house.
Look at funny Susan ! "

Uncle Fred and Aunt Mary laughed.

Mother and Father came out
of the house.

They looked at Susan, too.

Then they laughed.

Aunt Mary said,
" Little Susan is a big help, too.

She knows what to do.

What fun it is to come
to the little white house ! " 181

Our House

Our house is small —
The lawn and all
Can scarcely hold the flowers;
Yet every bit,
The whole of it,
Is precious, for it's ours!

From door to door,
From roof to floor,
From wall to wall we love it;
We wouldn't change
For something strange
One single corner of it!

The space complete
In cubic feet
From cellar floor to rafter
Just measures right,
And not too tight,
For us, and friends, and laughter !

Dorothy Brown Thompson

183

Words and Letters We Know

c h	d f	t m
color	farm	take
home	did	turkey
came	fun	mill
has	duck	me
g w	s b	l r
guess	some	little
walk	seven	run
good	but	race
went	barn	like
d p	h r	m g
duck	run	get
party	he	my
down	race	good
pets	hat	mouse
l t	f s	p b
toys	fast	barn
little	seven	paint
take	saw	boat
look	fun	put

Match each initial consonant with the correct words.

184

Words and Sentences

will	hen	not
hill	men	dot
bill	ten	got

1. Tom sees the ten white hens.

2. Where are the black hens?

red	get	dog
bed	let	fog
fed	pet	log

1. This dog is a good pet.

2. He will not get on the bed.

hat	run	can
cat	gun	Dan
fat	sun	man

1. The big cat likes the sun.

2. She will run to Dan.

Read the rhyming words and the sentences which follow them.

More Words and Sentences

ride	like	came
side	hike	tame
hide	mike	game

1. Nan and Betty like to hide.

2. They play a game with Tom.

cake	race	take
make	face	bake
lake	lace	rake

1. Mother will bake a cake.

2. We can take it to the lake.

look	me	go
book	we	so
took	he	no

1. Jack will look at my book.

2. He took it home.

Read the rhyming words and the sentences which follow them.

Choose the Right Word

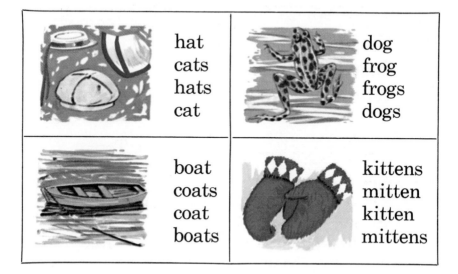

hat
cats
hats
cat

dog
frog
frogs
dogs

boat
coats
coat
boats

kittens
mitten
kitten
mittens

look
looked

1. Tom _____ at the new red truck.

jump
jumped

2. Flip will _____ out of the wagon.

walk
walked

3. Jack and Tom can _____ to the store.

help
helped

4. Betty _____ Mother with the work.

Find the correct word to go with each picture. Then read each
of the sentences, choosing the correct word to go in the blank.

Choose the Right Answer

Tiger ran to the tree.   Teddy
Up the tree he went.   Jip
Will he get down?   Father
Who will help Tiger?   Bunny

Bob likes new toys.   a pony
He went to the store.   a truck
He looked and looked.   a mill
What did Bob get?   a train

Tom went away.   a boat
He went to see Uncle Fred.   a truck
He saw Mr. Bell too.   a wagon
What did he ride on?   a train

Read and choose the right answer.

Answer Each Question

Who has a little kitten?	Betty
Who has Patsy?	Cathy
Who has Bunny?	Tom
Who has Flip?	Susan

Who has a truck?	Mr. Bell
Who has a farm?	Nancy
Who works on a train?	Uncle Fred
Who has a toy mouse?	Mr. Green

Who said " gobble " ?	the kitten
Who said " mew " ?	the children
Who said " quack " ?	the turkey
Who said " thank you " ?	the duck

Find the answer to each question.

Vocabulary List

This primer, *The Little White House*, follows the three basic pre-primers, *My Little Red Story Book*, Pre-Primer I; *My Little Green Story Book*, Pre-Primer II; and *My Little Blue Story Book*, Pre-Primer III, of the GINN BASIC READING SERIES. This Primer contains 100 new words. All the 62 words which the children learned in the pre-primers of this series are repeated in this book. The 13 words of *My Little Blue Story Book* are reintroduced on this primer level.

The lines in the list indicate the ending of one story or unit and the beginning of another.

New Words in This Book

Unit I
4 . . .
5 home
6 . . .
7 . . .
8 . . .

9 . . .
10 now
11 are
12 . . .

13 paint
14 ready
15 . . .
16 . . .

17 like
18 my
19 color
20 . . .
21 guess
22 . . .

23 in
24 box
25 white
26 good

27 . . .
28 . . .
29 . . .
30 . . .

Unit II
31 pets
32 hat
33 mew
34 kitten

35 will
36 run
37 tree
38 Tiger
39 please
40 do
41 went

42 he

43 bow-wow
44 away
45 . . .
46 did

47 cowboy
48 it
49 Mr.
50 truck
51 . . .
52 . . .

53 . . .
54 dog
55 then
56 zoom
57 children
58 . . .

Unit III
59 birthday

60 wagon
61 fun
62 saw
63 . . .
64 . . .

65 she
66 candles
67 . . .
68 put
69 party
70 seven

71 Nan
72 Jack
73 your
74 where
75 has
76 happy

77 Uncle
78 Fred
79 store

190

80 they	106 called	131 race	156 . . .
81 laughed	107 . . .	132 . . .	157 . . .
		133 . . .	158 . . .
82 know	108 . . .	134 . . .	
83 . . .	109 . . .		**Unit VII**
84 black	110 looked	**Unit VI**	159 . . .
85 with	111 . . .	135 . . .	160 . . .
86 train	112 . . .		161 . . .
	113 . . .	136 yellow	162 . . .
Unit IV	114 . . .	137 some	163 . . .
87 farm		138 of	164 . . .
88 on	115 ducks	139 . . .	
89 aunt	116 water	140 who	165 . . .
90 Mary	117 came		166 . . .
91 Bell	118 . . .	141 out	167 . . .
		142 . . .	168 . . .
92 too	**Unit V**	143 . . .	169 . . .
93 . . .	119 new	144 walked	170 . . .
94 jumped	120 walk	145 . . .	171 . . .
95 thank	121 quack	146 . . .	172 . . .
96 . . .	122 . . .		
97 barn		147 hen	173 . . .
98 me	123 mouse	148 wheat	174 . . .
99 eat	124 . . .	149 plant	175 . . .
100 . . .	125 . . .	150 mill	176 . . .
	126 . . .	151 bread	
101 turkey		152 . . .	177 . . .
102 take	127 boat	153 . . .	178 . . .
103 gobble	128 . . .		179 . . .
104 but	129 . . .	154 yes	180 . . .
105 ran	130 . . .	155 may	181 . . .

Reintroduction of Pre-Primer III Words

9 big	18 blue	38 up	89 Patsy
11 funny	20 what	43 play	
12 not	22 have	57 house	
17 little	23 down	63 make	

Acknowledgments

Grateful acknowledgment is made to the following authors and publishers for permission to adapt copyrighted materials:

Child Life magazine and Dorothy Brown Thompson for the poem *Our House*, by Dorothy Brown Thompson, copyright 1939; Coward-McCann, Inc., for "The Toy Mouse," based on a story in *The Cautious Carp*, by Nicholas Radlov, copyright, 1938, by Coward-McCann, Inc.; The Platt & Munk Co., Inc., for "In the Barn," adapted from "The Visit" in *Mother Stories and More Mother Stories* by Maud Lindsay; Rand McNally & Company, for "Who Is Big," adapted from *Vickie, the Chick*, by Martha Cranford; copyright 1951, by Rand McNally & Company, publishers.

SPECIAL ACKNOWLEDGMENT for advice and assistance in the preparation of this edition is made to Edna W. Morgan, Chief of the Bureau of Reading Education for the New York State Education Department at Albany, New York.

ILLUSTRATIONS BY Harry Anderson, Ed. Gordon, Margo Pisillo, and Alex Ross.

B C D E F G H I J 06987
PRINTED IN THE UNITED STATES OF AMERICA